Unit 2
Our Families, Our Neighbors

Contents

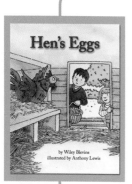

Week 3

Show What You Know

This and That

by Meish Goldish
illustrated by Melissa Sweet

Fox on a Rock

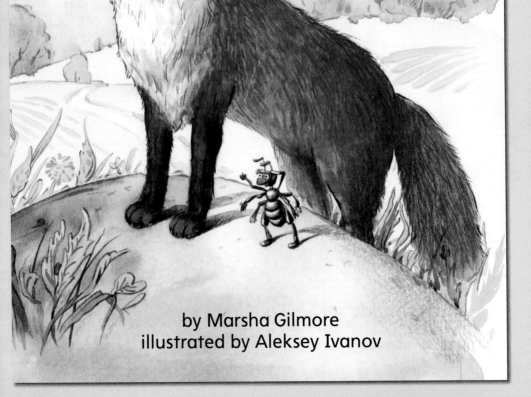

by Marsha Gilmore
illustrated by Aleksey Ivanov

Mom Fox is very sad.
Where is Bob Fox now?

Is Bob Fox in Frog's pond?
Bob is not in Frog's pond.

Is Bob Fox in Tom's box?
Bob is not in Tom's box.

Mom Fox is sad.
Mom sits on a rock.
Mom can use help.

Ant can help Mom Fox.
Now Mom can see Bob Fox!

Moms and Dads

Cat Moms

A cat mom can lick.

A cat mom can hop.

A cat mom can do a lot!

7

Dog Dads

A dog dad can dig.

A dog dad can sit on top.

A dog dad has a big job!

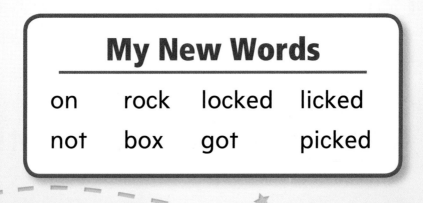

My New Words

on	rock	locked	licked
not	box	got	picked

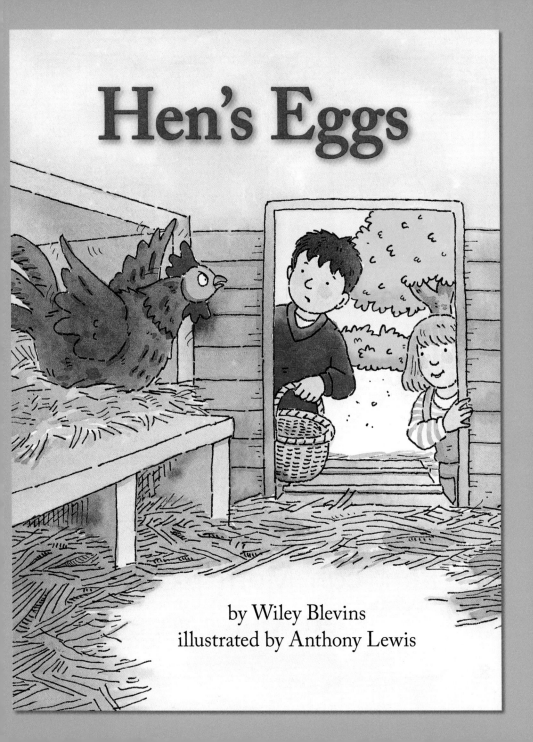

Hen's Eggs

by Wiley Blevins
illustrated by Anthony Lewis

"Ben, can Mom fix eggs?"
"Yes, Meg. Get two eggs."

"We have one egg.
Get Hen's egg, Ben."

Does Hen have eggs?
Ben is in her pen.
Hen is mad!

Meg yells for Mom and Dad.
They will help.

Splat!
Mom will not fix eggs.
Mom will fix ham!

The Hen and the Pig

Hen
Hen will dig and plant. Hen will get the wheat. Hen will mix and mix. Hen will eat bread!

Pig

Pig will not dig and plant.
Pig will sit and rest.
Pig will not help Hen mix.
Pig can't eat Hen's bread!

My New Words

best	yes	yell	isn't
went	vest	let's	aren't

Pet Tricks

by Ed Reyes
illustrated by Joe Cepeda

Who can do a trick?
A lot of pets can!

Frizz has a trick.
Frizz can skip over a bat.

Ham can do some tricks.
Ham can run on a track.

Spot has a trick.
Spot can grab a rope.
Spot can spin.

Can Kit do a trick?
No, Kit can not.
But Kit can kiss.
It is a good trick!

22

Use a Map

Greg and Stef can use a map.

Greg can spot a place to swim.

It has sand and grass and frogs!

Stef can spot a place to get stamps.
It has red bricks and a clock.
What can you spot on a map?

My New Words

stop	grip	rocking	mixing
stand	brag	fixing	yelling

Gus and Fluff

by Adin Shapiro
illustrated by Javier Gonzalez

Gus and Fluff live in a
fun place.
It has many nuts.

Gus and Fluff sit on
nuts.

Gus and Fluff set
nuts up.

Gus and Fluff eat nuts.

"Let us go out," said Gus.
"Yes," said Fluff.
"Let us get nuts!"

The Big Mud Hut

Pigs sit in a mud hut.

Pigs run and jump
in mud.

Pigs hop and plop
in mud.

Pigs will not let
Big Bad Wolf in.

Big Bad Wolf huffs and puffs.
Big Bad Wolf kicks the hut in.
Big Bad Wolf can't stand a big mess!
Big Bad Wolf runs off.

My New Words

us	must	truck	just	it's
but	sun	drum	she's	he's

This and That

by Meish Goldish
illustrated by Melissa Sweet

Seth had a red can.
What could Seth make?
Thump, thump, thump!

Tim had a red lid.
Thud, thud, thud!

Beth had a flat dish.
Crash, crash, crash!

"Again!" Seth said.
One, two, three!
Thump, thud, crash!

Think of things to hit.
Then hit this and that.
Thump, thud, crash!

38

A Band for Kids

Bud and Ann

Bud can hit a tub with sticks.
Bud can rap, tap, tap!
Ann can play a jug.
Ann can make that jug hum!

Will and Beth

Will can bang two
lids together.

Will can crush and crash
the lids.

Beth can sing a song.
Beth is tops at singing!

My New Words

thick	math	shop	fish	bathtub
thank	blink	long	swing	sunset

Unit 2: Our Families, Our Neighbors

to use with *Animal Moms and Dads*   **WORD COUNT: 58**

DECODABLE WORDS

Target Phonics Element

short *o*

Bob, box, Fox, Frog's, Mom, not, on, pond, rock, Tom's

Words Using Previously Taught Skills

a, Ant, can, in, is, sad, sits

HIGH-FREQUENCY WORDS

Review: help, now, see, use, very, where

SHOW WHAT YOU KNOW: Moms and Dads

DECODABLE WORDS

Target Phonics Elements

short *o*

inflectional ending *-ed*

box, dog, got, hop, job, licked, locked, lot, mom, moms, not, on, picked, rock, top

to use with *Little Red Hen*   **WORD COUNT: 49**

DECODABLE WORDS

Target Phonics Element

short *e*

Ben, egg(s), get, help, Hen, Hen's, Meg, pen, yells, yes

Words Using Previously Taught Skills

and, can, Dad, fix, ham, in, is, mad, Mom, not, splat, will

HIGH-FREQUENCY WORDS

Review: for, have, her, they, two, we

STORY WORDS

does, one

SHOW WHAT YOU KNOW: The Hen and the Pig

DECODABLE WORDS

Target Phonics Elements

short *e*

contractions

aren't, best, get, help, Hen, isn't, let's, rest, vest, went, yell, yes

42

to use with *On the Map*

WORD COUNT: 61

DECODABLE WORDS
Target Phonics Elements
s blends
  skip, spin, Spot
r blends
  Frizz, grab, track, trick(s)

Words Using Previously Taught Skills
a, bat, can, Ham, has, is, it, kiss, Kit, lot, not, on, pet(s)

HIGH-FREQUENCY WORDS
Review: do, good, no, of, over, some, who

STORY WORDS
but, rope, run

SHOW WHAT YOU KNOW: Use a Map

DECODABLE WORDS
Target Phonics Elements
r blends, *s* blends
inflectional ending -*ing*
  brag, bricks, fixing, frogs, grass, Greg, grip, mixing, rocking, spot, stamps, stand, Stef, stop, swim, yelling

43

to use with *The Pigs, the Wolf, and the Mud*   **WORD COUNT: 42**

DECODABLE WORDS

Target Phonics Element

short *u*

Fluff, fun, Gus, nuts, up, us

Words Using Previously Taught Skills

a, and, get, has, in, it, let, on, set, sit, yes

HIGH-FREQUENCY WORDS

Review: eat, go, live, many, out, place, said

SHOW WHAT YOU KNOW: The Big Mud Hut

DECODABLE WORDS

Target Phonics Elements

short *u*

contractions with *-s*

but, drum, he's, huffs, hut, it's, jump, just, mud, must, puffs, run(s), she's, sun, truck, us

to use with *Beth and the Band*

WORD COUNT: 50

DECODABLE WORDS

Target Phonics Elements

digraph *sh*

crash, dish

digraph *th*

Beth, Seth, that, then, things, think, this, thud, thump

digraph *ng*

things

Words Using Previously Taught Skills

a, and, can, had, hit, flat, lid, red, Tim

HIGH-FREQUENCY WORDS

Review: again, could, make, of, one, said, three, to, two, what

SHOW WHAT YOU KNOW: A Band for Kids

DECODABLE WORDS

Target Phonics Elements

digraphs *sh*, *th*, *ng*

compound words

bang, bathtub, Beth, blink, crash, crush, fish, long, math, shop, sing, singing, song, sunset, swing, thank, that, thick, with

HIGH-FREQUENCY WORDS TAUGHT TO DATE

Grade K	Grade I	
a	again	too
and	all	two
are	be	under
can	come	up
do	could	use
for	down	very
go	eat	want
has	good	who
have	help	
he	her	
here	it	
I	jump	
is	live	
like	make	
little	many	
look	no	
me	not	
my	now	
play	of	
said	one	
see	our	
she	out	
the	over	
this	place	
to	pull	
was	put	
we	ride	
what	run	
where	show	
with	some	
you	then	
	they	
	three	
	together	

DECODING SKILLS TAUGHT TO DATE

CVC letter patterns; short *a*; consonants *b, c, ck, f, g, h, k, l, m, n, p, r, s, t, v;* inflectional ending *-s* (plurals, verbs); short *i*; consonants *d, j, qu, w, x, y, z;* double final consonants; *l* blends; possessives with *'s;* end blends; short *o;* inflectional ending *-ed;* short *e;* contractions with *n't; s* blends; *r* blends; inflectional ending *-ing;* short *u;* contractions with *'s;* digraphs *sh, th, ng;* compound words